Year after Year

Year after Year

by Bill Binzen

Coward, McCann & Geoghegan · New York

For Peter & Virginia

Excerpts from Poem #22, "All these my banners be,"
and Poem #1644, "Some one prepared this mighty
show," reprinted by permission of the publishers and
the Trustees of Amherst College from THE POEMS
OF EMILY DICKINSON, edited by Thomas H.
Johnson, Cambridge, Massachusetts: The Belknap
Press of Harvard University Press, Copyright © 1951,
1955 by the President and Fellows of Harvard College.

SBN: GB-698-30613-9 SBN: TR-698-20361-5
Library of Congress Catalog Card Number: 76-27615
Printed in the United States of America

Designed by Leslie Bauman

And the earth, they tell me,
On its axis turned,—
Wonderful rotation
By but twelve performed!

Spring

You and I the secret
Of the crocus know—
Let us chant it softly—
"There is no more snow!"

Summer

❖————————————————————————❖

Some one prepared this mighty show
To which without a ticket go
The nations and the days—

Displayed before the simplest door
That all may witness it and more,
The pomp of summer days.

❖————————————————————————❖

Fall

❖───────────────────────────❖

Frequently the woods are pink,
Frequently are brown;
Frequently the hills undress
Behind my native town.

❖───────────────────────────❖

Winter

There's a certain slant of light,
On winter afternoons,
That oppresses, like the weight
Of cathedral tunes.

And still the pensive spring returns,
And still the punctual snow!